Big Hair

by **Heather Pindar**

illustrated by **Marina Pessarrodona**

When Dan got out of bed he had...

...BIG HAIR.

"No! No! No!" said Dan.

"I can NOT go to school looking like this!"

Dan put his head under the tap.

He got his hair all wet.

But his hair was still BIG!

Dan stood on his head, but...

...his hair got BIGGER!

14

Dan put on
a tight hat.

15

But it pinged off.

And his hair got

even BIGGER!

Dan set off to school.

He hid in the bushes.

He crept into class.

"Look at Dan!" said Jack.

"He's got BIG HAIR!"

"Wow! Cool hair!" said Jim.

"It's FANTASTIC!" said Binta.

Emma put some pegs in her hair.

"Now I've got BIG HAIR too!"

said Emma.

Adnan shook his head like a dog.

"Me too!" said Adnan.

Soon everyone had BIG HAIR.

"I hear footsteps," said Adnan.

"Help! Here comes Miss Crimp!"

Everyone stood still.

"Good morning!" said Miss Crimp.

Quiz

1. When Dan woke up, he had...
a) Flat hair
b) Big hair
c) Small hair

2. What did Dan do first?
a) Put his head under the tap
b) Go to school
c) Put on a tight hat

3. Where did Dan hide?
a) At home
b) In the bushes
c) Behind his dog

4. What does Emma put in her hair?

a) Water

b) A mop

c) Pegs

5. What does everyone in Dan's class do?

a) Make Dan's hair smaller

b) Go home

c) Get big hair

Turn over for answers

Book Bands for Guided Reading

The Institute of Education book banding system is a scale of colours that reflects the various levels of reading difficulty. The bands are assigned by taking into account the content, the language style, the layout and phonics. Word, phrase and sentence level work is also taken into consideration.

Maverick Early Readers are a bright, attractive range of books covering the pink to white bands. All of these books have been book banded for guided reading to the industry standard and edited by a leading educational consultant.

To view the whole Maverick Readers scheme, visit our website at
www.maverickearlyreaders.com

Or scan the QR code above to view our scheme instantly!

Pink
Red
Yellow
Blue
Green
Orange
Turquoise
Purple
Gold
White